Ducky's Surprise

Illustrated by Don Stuart
Story concept by Gail Tuchman

SCHOLASTIC INC.
New York   Toronto   London   Auckland   Sydney
Mexico City   New Delhi   Hong Kong   Buenos Aires

2

3

5

6

Illustrations copyright © 2003 by Don Stuart.
All rights reserved. Published by Scholastic Inc.
Printed in the U.S.A.

ISBN 0-439-53344-9

SCHOLASTIC, SCHOLASTIC READINGLINE, and associated logos and designs
are trademarks and/or registered trademarks of Scholastic Inc.

1 2 3 4 5 6 7 8 9 10   23   14 13 12 11 10 09 08 07 06 05